P

20 V ... ice

To:

C

The light in me
honors the light in
you.
Namaste,
Dianne

Pathways to Peace: Visualizations to Enhance Your Yoga Practice

ISBN: 979-8-9855551-0-3 (pbk)
ISBN: 979-8-9855551-1-0 (ebook)

Printed in the U.S.A.

Thank you for purchasing Pathways to Peace: 20 Visualizations to Enhance your Yoga Practice.

I would like to show my appreciation for purchasing this book with this free video demonstrating yoga poses integrated with one of the visualizations featured in the book!

Go to Pathways to Peace free gift (https://www.subscribepage.com/k6s2n6)and begin your Pathway to Peace now!

This book is dedicated to…

My loving and supportive family; Paul, Jeff, Natasha, Jake, Abby, and my grandchildren, Carson, Bentley, and Baby March 2022. May your pathway to peace be fulfilling and fruitful.

Embrace the Journey.

—Unknown

TABLE OF CONTENTS

Introduction

Every single day! Every day, I would set aside time in the morning for meditation, prayer, centering time, or whatever you would like to call it. I would count my blessings, (yes, and write them down), read a daily reflection, ask God for help throughout the day, and sit quietly. Breath practice was integrated in all of it! I would leave the house feeling peaceful, confident, and focused. Boom! Then it all went out the window within five minutes of getting to work. I was overwhelmed, in a hurry, and distracted. I felt like all I did all day was run around doing my "to-do" list, plus everyone else's. Why couldn't I maintain the sense of peace I had felt less than 30 minutes before? Why was it so hard to maintain? I tried to regain my focus. Thinking I needed reminders throughout the day, I would set my phone alarm and take a few minutes to go to my window and take five deep breaths or stretch for a few minutes. But then I would be off to the races again, distracted, busy, and tense.

I felt lost, tired, and frustrated with myself. I had raised my children and been an empty nester for a year or so. Shouldn't it be easier to maintain a sense of peace and focus now that I didn't have so many demands on my time like extracurricular events, people to feed, endless loads of laundry, finding time to check in and connect with each child and my spouse? It should be easy, right? Instead, I found myself feeling tired, lost, and frustrated much of the time. My life had become a list of things to do at work, at home, for others. I didn't have a direction, except for those few moments of focus each morning. How could I get myself out of this endless cycle?

Being a reflective person by nature, I began looking back at strategies I had utilized other times in my life when I was feeling stuck. One of the biggest game changers in my life was when I started to practice yoga. Although I loved to work out, I had resisted yoga for a long time. I preferred aerobics, weight lifting, cross training, running, and walking. I needed to be active; I needed to move. It was part of how I managed my stress. Yoga, at least how I had experienced it up until that time, was not fast enough nor intense enough. Nevertheless, I did it because into my life came, almost simultaneously, acute back pain and, a phenomenal yoga teacher I could connect with.

I began doing yoga after my "intense" workout one day a week as my "treat" for the weekend. My children were small, and this time of quiet was welcomed and luxurious. My muscles deserved it after all my intense workouts that week, besides lugging around children and bags and everything else. I went through a period when the only exercise I could do without causing more back pain was walking and yoga. I was convinced I would gain weight, become stressed out, and experience a lack of energy or depression. Imagine my surprise when the opposite occurred. I discovered yoga could be very intense, maintain my weight, and have calming effects on both my mental and physical health.

I credit my yoga teacher at that time (and still 20 years after) with the release from physical and mental stress. It was the first time anyone had taught me how to breathe during exercise, and breath practice calmed both my mind and body. She taught more of a flow type of yoga than what I had experienced before, and balanced movement with stillness in a manner which with I connected. But the biggest contribution she made to my practice was the use of visualization, both during poses and in stillness.

During poses, she might suggest you were cracking a walnut between your shoulder blades or pushing the floor away from your hands (yes, I now realize these are common cues, but they were earth shattering to me at the time). In stillness, she might suggest you were talking with a person you hadn't seen in a while and what did you need to say, or you were at your favorite place in nature and what did you see, hear, or feel. This exposure to having control over my breath, body, and thoughts was both new and inspiring to me. I latched on.

I continued to practice with this teacher for many years, and when her business expanded to include a school of yoga, I eventually became a 200-hour yoga certified teacher myself. This deepened my understanding of proper form, and it exposed me to the eight limbs of yoga. I taught on and off over the next few years, with interruptions caused by back surgery, a broken humerus, and carpal tunnel surgery. I finally had a consistent number of students in my classes and refueled weekly as a student in a Saturday morning class when along came closures due to the COVID19 Pandemic.

During the COVID pandemic closures, I relied largely on YouTube videos and my own previously created classes for my yoga practice. I was grateful for this, yet noticed most, if not all, YouTube classes addressed only one limb of yoga, the asanas or poses. Sometimes, they included something about breath (pranayama limb), and once in a great while, they would mention an intention. At first, I added the other elements before and/or after the video: pranayama, relieving my sense of external distractions (pratyahara), and becoming internally more focused, dharana. Journaling and quiet time helped me observe niyama elements, such as keeping a clear mental state, staying grounded, being fully present to move toward self-realization (tapas), and self-study to deepen my spiritual sense. Yes, at first, I was able to practice these elements, but as time passed, I found myself leaving less and less time for this, and my own practice became almost solely focused on poses. I noticed a change in myself, I was less focused, felt agitated and irritated more often, doubted my purpose, and periods of depression and anxiety occurred more frequently.

This is where I was when society began to open up after the pandemic and I found myself returning to work in person. I committed to maintaining my morning reflection time but found myself in the state described at the beginning of this chapter. What needed changing? I set out with a goal of increasing focus on my priorities, decreasing distractions and anxiety, and living in the moment.

I was reminded of the story about the jar of rice and the golf balls. Given a jar full of rice and five golf balls, the challenge was offered to fit the golf balls in the jar without spilling any of the rice. Impossible, so one might think. The person offering the challenge then calmly pours the rice into a container, places the golf balls in the jar first, then pours the rice back into the jar without spilling any. Success. I had been filling my life, and my days at work specifically, with rice first, running around to complete tasks and make life easier for others, and there was no room for any golf balls, or priorities. This was why I was feeling distracted, overwhelmed, and agitated much of the time. I had to find a way to first choose my priorities, put them in the jar first, and finally, let all the other pieces fall into place around them.

Practicing meditation with visualization in my yoga practice became my vehicle for this. The yoga studio's reopening after COVID closures was a huge reminder about the other limbs of yoga. We were allowed to do a minimal of breath practice due to wearing masks, so I decided I would work on this at home. During breath practice, I again began to focus on intentions, which led me to the path of attaching images to the intentions. As an educator, I knew that the more senses attached to something to be remembered, the more pathways for accessing and, thus, remembering it. I began creating sequences where I created a visual and mental focus for my practice in the beginning, used physical and mental connections throughout, and reconnected with the visualization during savasana or resting pose.

The exercises in this book are designed to provide you with a tool for increasing focus through the integration of visualization with breath and physical poses to deepen your own personal practice and/or that of your students. Applying them will assist in maintaining a sense of purpose and intentionality in your practice and life. This will promote a sense of focus and wellness transferable to all areas of your life.

I have been practicing yoga over 18 years, instructing a range of classes for over five years, and integrating visualizations to different degrees throughout all this time. Since I've been using the visualizations consistently, I've noticed a deeper sense of calm and focus in myself, resulting in higher productivity at work and in my personal life. I have increased energy (as evidenced by being able to write this book while juggling an intense career and balancing family), reduced anxiety, and am less easily distracted and more focused on the present moment. Read and utilize the visualizations in this book if you desire to integrate visualizations seamlessly into your yoga practice and/or teaching

Choose visualizations for a purpose, including to increase focus, experience gratitude, let go of the past or negativity, increase self-confidence, and enhance sleep or relaxation. Deepen your yoga practice by expanding on the limbs of yoga.

Visualization Benefits:

The benefits of visualization have been known for a long time. Perhaps, for me, the most important of these is that visualization fosters a sense of purpose. When you know what you want and visualize the steps to get there, your energies will follow. Energy goes where attention flows, so visualizing can increase your focus on what's important to you, whether it be an internal factor, such as trust or peace, or an external factor, such as a job, achievement, or material possession. You'll find that the more you focus on it, the more your energy and, therefore, your actions will gravitate toward it, moving you forward. Simultaneously, visualization decreases negativity. When you visualize and move toward your goal, you allow less room in your brain for self-doubt and anxiety.

Visualization allows for creativity by releasing our minds from busy, overscheduled, monotonous routines of life. It allows for a change to your mindset, providing a break from social constructs that keep you stuck. This fosters an increased sense of courage. During visualizations, your brain builds hormones and synapses similar to those that would be created if you were actually performing the action. This fools your brain into thinking you have already done or accomplished what you're visualizing. Since you're no longer viewing the action as new or different and have brain activity to support the action, you're more confident moving forward (Janesksela, 2018).

Visualization as a means to achievement is supported by brain research. The neurons in our brains interpret imagery as the same as real life action. When you visualize being by a river, on a nature walk, taking an action toward a goal, performing a yoga pose, or being filled with a sense of peace, a new neural pathway is created. These clusters of cells that create memories or learned behaviors cause our body to remember this state of being, making it more accessible the next time (Niles, 2011).

Furthermore, brain research supports that the more senses you associate with an idea, the more ways your brain has to retrieve the information. Using visualizations during yoga incorporates seeing, hearing, and touching at the very minimal, some add the sense of smell as well. A sight, sound, or pose (touch) can bring you back to an intention or feeling of peace and well-being you reached at a previous time, such as during a yoga practice. This triggers the same positive benefits to your body and mind experienced previously, maximizing the return of the time and energy you have already invested in your physical and mental well-being.

After applying the strategies in this book, I promise you'll be able to deepen your yoga practice, decrease anxiety, and increase the likelihood of achieving any goal or intention. If one of your priorities or "golf balls" is your mental and physical health, this book can help, and the time is now. With the rising incidences of mental health issues both before, during, and continuing through the ongoing pandemic, individuals need as many effective tools as possible to promote positive health of the body, mind, and spirit. The cost of ignoring these issues is too high. Establish your physical and mental health as your priority and let the rice fall into place around it.

The yoga limbs of breath, poses (asanas), and meditation have all been around for thousands of years in different capacities. All have been shown to have positive, lasting effects on physical, mental, and emotional health. Find out and practice how you can get "more bang for your buck" by deepening them all simultaneously during your yoga practice. The visualizations will help you to be your best self.

How to use this book:

For Yoga teachers:

Use this book to extend your yoga practice and teaching. The exercises combine breath, poses, and meditation. You may choose the meditations in any order; some of them will speak to you more than others. Of course, you'll incorporate your own perspective. The exercises are a guide or can be used verbatim. You might use the same visualization for several sequential classes, allowing students to more deeply integrate the visualization and focus, and experience the same visualization in a different sequence of poses. Or, you might pick a different visualization for each class, providing your students with a variety of options for deepening their practice based on their needs. You know your students, so do what's most appropriate for them.

The visualization exercises are divided into five categories: Self-confidence, Focus/Engagement, Gratitude, Letting Go, and Relaxation. There's some overlap in the categories, but I tried to fit each visualization into where it aligned most naturally. For example, a visualization that helps students let go of stress and worries will naturally help them relax their bodies and minds and could therefore fit in the relaxation chapter too. A visualization that helps students to let go also provides increased opportunities for focus. So, be flexible with your thinking and choose an exercise that aligns with your intent for the class, whether it fits neatly into a subcategory or not!

Each visualization contains these sections:

Setting the Stage: Introducing the visualization

Connections during your practice: Suggests general cues that might be used in different poses, often centering around inhale/exhale or contract/release.

Examples: Cues connected to the visualization to be used with specific poses. Warrior II is used in every visualization to provide consistency. At least one other pose is provided to demonstrate how some visualizations lend themselves more naturally to a specific pose.

Your Turn: Time for you to write specific cues for the poses you plan to use in your class or session based on the visualization.

Closing: Reflection and relaxation (Intended to be used for savasana, but use as you see fit).

Booster: This is a short 1-2-sentence affirmation aligned with the visualization for your students to take with them to help them reconnect with their practice as they return to the "real world."

Variations: There are some ideas for modifications to the visualization to make them more or less specific, and to provide some flexibility.

As the instructor, there may be situations when you would use only one or two sections; go for it! Again, like everything in yoga, the instructor and the students make choices along the way! You know your students, your intent, and the poses you intend to include. Make it work for your needs.

My recommendation for planning your classes is as follows:

- Consider target audience/students
- Select the visualization
- Plan your poses/vinyasa
- Practice
- Make adjustments
- Deliver
- Reflect

For the Non-Yoga teacher:

The visualization exercises may be used in any situation when either yourself or others seek the benefits of visualization. As mentioned earlier in this chapter, visualization and meditation help with enhancing creativity, increasing focus, reducing anxiety, and promoting a sense of well-being. In addition to personal use, others who might utilize this resource are counselors, spiritual leaders, trainers, and professional development providers.

The following are suggested steps for utilizing these exercises in other situations:

Section 1: (Setting the stage)

Section 2: Instead of how to use them in your practice, you might use the suggestions in this section to provide a challenge to use a piece of the visualization throughout the day (e.g., when life gets chaotic, visualize a calming shade of your color spectrum). Or simply pause and go to the next section.

Section 3: Closing connections

Again, make it work for your needs, and the needs of those you're guiding.

Disclaimer: henceforth, when I refer to "your needs," this includes both personal and/or the audience (students, clients, participants, employees) for which you intend to use it.

Focus & Engage

"Concentration can be cultivated. One can learn to exercise will power, discipline one's body and train one's mind."

–Anil Ambani

Color Spectrum

Setting the Stage:

Select a color that's meaningful or pleasing to you. See the color from its softest hues, gradually becoming stronger and brighter until it reaches its most intense, vibrant version. Now gradually reverse it, so that it becomes slightly lighter and lighter until it's again at its softest hue. Think of this spectrum of color as an analogy for your practice today. We have begun with calming our breathing, thus, the color at its lightest shade. We will gradually warm our bodies in our poses, and the color will become more vibrant as the poses intensify, until we arrive at our peak pose, which aligns with the most vibrant shade of that color. Eventually, we'll gradually decrease the intensity of our poses, just as the color fades back to its softest or calmest version.

During our practice, continually visualize the color at some shade in its spectrum, aligned with the intensity of the pose. Another possibility is that the most strongly engaged parts of your body correlate with the strongest hues, and the relaxed or less engaged parts align with a softer shade. At other times, we breathe through a strong, challenging pose, with the first breaths at the most intense shade, and as our body relaxes into the pose, the color travels a few shades down the spectrum. Correspondingly, as the color travels down the spectrum, it allows us to relax more deeply into the pose.

Connections during your practice:

Inhale, see a vibrant shade, on the exhale, gradually let the color fade down to its softest version as your lungs empty.

Contract and release: As you contract your muscles, the color is intense. As you release the muscles, the color fades slowly down the spectrum.

Specific poses; visualize an intense version of the color where your body is most engaged, and a softer shade where it's less engaged.

Examples:

Warrior II (Virabhadrasana II)

See the strong, vibrant color in the engagement of your core as your navel firms toward your spine, in the little toe side of your back foot as it pushes into the floor, in your inner thighs as they push toward each other, in the big toe as it pushes down for balance, and in the strength of your shoulder blades as they move away from your ears and support your extended arms.

Visualize a softer color in the buoyancy of your arms, and the very softest of shades in your relaxed facial muscles as your gaze focuses ahead.

Forward Fold (Uttanasana)

Envision a strong color throughout your feet as they push down into the floor as your base, up your calves, softer through the knees, strong in the quads, and throughout your core as it engages upward. The shade in your shoulders, arms, and hands is softer, perhaps a hue in the middle of the spectrum, as you let go and hang, and the very lightest hues in your neck muscles as it works freely to relax downward with gravity.

Plank pose (Kumbhakasana)

Check that you have the strongest shade visualized in your hands, feet, and core. Make sure that the color, and your weight, is equally distributed throughout your palms and fingers, and feet. The rest of your body is also engaged, but the color is slightly less intense on the spectrum; still strong and yet weaker than your hands, feet, and core. As you inhale, see the color traveling throughout and around your body, strongest in the parts connecting with your mat; on the exhale let it push out and back through your heels.

Your turn: Choose some of the key poses that are part of your practice today. In a notebook, write specifically the words you would use to help your students utilize this visualization to enhance the pose and focus the mind.

Closing:

Consider the most relaxing shade of your color. Let it fill your vision, calming your body. Imagine the color on your forehead, calming your thoughts. Gradually, let it move down your body to your neck, relaxing each of those muscles. See it continue to your upper torso, shoulders, elbows, arms, and fingers, as well as your lower torso and core, releasing each muscle. If you find a point where the color is more intense because of tightness or tension in your body, stop on that spot. Envision the color getting softer and softer in and around that muscle, causing it to let go of the tension. Let the color continue down through your hips, upper thighs, kneecaps, calves, ankles, and finally, your toes.

The calming color now encompasses your entire body, relaxing each muscle. The color also fills your mind, relaxing every thought and concern. If a worry or concern makes its way back into your mind, the calming color releases it. Every muscle is relaxed, and your mind is filled with calmness. Your breath comes in and out, calming your entire being, filling every inch of your body and mind. It will be silent for 3-5 minutes now for you to simply be in this state. [Pause 3-5 minutes, depending on time]

Gradually open your eyes, blinking as you feel the sense of peace and see the calming color. Awaken your body. Even though you're coming back to the physical, mental, and emotional world around you, the calmness stays within you and surrounds your being.

Give yourself permission to take this color with you throughout your day, allowing the softest shades to calm your mind when needed, and increasing its vibrance when you need to engage more energy.

Namaste

Booster:

I control where I focus my energy.

Variations:

Use the color spectrum exclusively with the breathing aspect. Begin at an inhale as the soft color, hold at the top in the most vibrant color, and with the slow exhale, channel down through the spectrum, holding for a count with your lungs empty and the softest color. To experiment, take an inhale that moves immediately from soft to its most intense and back again, symbolizing a panic breath or how we are often breathing in our hurried, everyday life. Work at visualizing the slow spectrum change for intense moments in our lives. If you have a particular person, situation, or event that you're struggling with, commit to changing your reaction next time by using this visualization.

Use the color spectrum on one particular part of your body that's causing you discomfort or pain. The point of discomfort is symbolized by the most intense color. Inhale to visualize this hue, and on a slow exhale, the hue decreases as the discomfort decreases at the same pace as the color traveling down the spectrum. On your next inhale, begin with the ending shade of your last exhale, and repeat the process of decreasing the discomfort in accordance with the intensity of the color along the spectrum. Repeat this process as many times as needed to release the discomfort.

Breathing with Balloons

Setting the Stage:

Start in standing, seated, or supine.

Become aware of your breath, not trying to change or lengthen it but accepting it and yourself as it is.

Take a couple of cleansing breaths, in your nose and out your mouth.

Gently close your eyes or look down at the tip of your nose and start to deepen your breath. Imagine a balloon in your stomach. Slowly fill the balloon with a slow inhale and release the air slowly as you exhale. After you've done that a few times, experiment with the opposite. Breathe in quickly, which doesn't allow the balloon to fill fully, and exhale at a rapid rate, which causes the balloon to go flying in all directions. Often in our lives, our breathing is like this, adding to the chaos of our surroundings and our lives.

Return to those slow, deep inhales, slowly filling up the balloon, and then slowly, gradually release the air until the balloon is completely empty. This brings calmness to our breath and our life.

Choose an intention for your practice today, a word or image that's desirable to you. Words might include peace, tranquility, or focus; images could entail a sunrise or sunset, the crackling of a fire, or a waterfall. Whatever speaks to you, envision filling the balloon in your abdomen with it as you inhale, and gradually releasing it to let your intention touch all parts of your being as you exhale.

Remember your breath throughout your practice today, in moments of tension or challenge imagine filling and emptying the balloon in your belly slowly to return to a sense of calm and reconnect with your intention.

Gradually open your eyes and return to the room around you. Focus your gaze, your breath, and your intention.

As you start to move, remind yourself to breathe so that you completely fill the balloon, and to control your exhale by slowly releasing the air to maintain calmness.

Connecting throughout your practice:

Inhale to fill the balloon with your intention, exhale it slowly to touch all parts of you. Remember if you exhale too quickly, the balloon flies haphazardly and creates chaos.

Pause after providing cues for a specific pose for 5-8 breaths, asking students to watch or feel their abdomen rise and fall as their long breaths fill their lungs, and allow them to empty. Similarly, they're filling their mind and surrounding their being with their intention as they inhale and exhale.

Examples:

Warrior II (Virabhadrasana II)

Drop your hands to form a diamond shape over your abdomen, taking long breaths to fill and empty the abdomen, similar to a balloon. As your breath continues, return your arms to traditional Warrior II, looking over your front fingertips. With a strong core, continue to feel that strong, slow breath rise and fall in your stomach, while gazing over your front fingertips and focusing on your intention.

Warrior III (Virbhadrasana III)

Stand in the middle of the mat with feet together. Arrive at Warrior III by placing your hands in prayer at your chest, plant one foot into the floor, pressing down with the big toe, and find that "balloon breath" in your core to keep you stable. Slowly, tip forward until your torso is parallel with the floor, finding a focal point slightly in front of you that brings to mind your intention: Remaining focused on the breath, take the hand position of your choice and slowly fill and empty the balloon in your core. Notice if you wobble, the breath becomes chaotic, similar to the balloon that flew all over. Keep an even inhale and exhale to remain steady.

Your turn: Choose some of the key poses that are part of your practice today. In a notebook, write specifically the words you would use to help your students utilize this visualization to enhance the pose and focus the mind.

Closing:

Lying on your back with your legs dropping open, place your hands in a diamond shape over your abdomen again. Take a cleansing breath in the nose, and out the mouth, causing the balloon to become a little crazy again. Take a long inhale to the count of 6 to inflate the balloon, and a slow exhale of 8 to gradually release the air and calm the body. Do this for two or three rounds [pause], then either keep your hands on the belly or let them fall by your sides palms up. Revisit your intention for your practice today, appreciating both the physical breath practice with the balloon, and the mental focus on your intent. In the next few quiet moments, let your thoughts slowly come and go with your breath.

Before coming out of savasana, commit to taking both the breath practice and your intention into your daily life. Visualize those moments that sometimes get chaotic and imagine slowly filling and emptying the balloon to resist the chaos. Picture when it will be important to see and fill your body with your intention and set the focus on your intention as your priority.

Begin to awaken your body [cues]...

Namaste

Booster:

I can use my breath to resist chaos and remain focused.

Variations:

Identify a specific place of tension in the body or that's activated in a pose. Imagine the balloon is there, and you're slowly inhaling and exhaling into that location, using the breath to release the tension or relax deeper into the pose.

Focus through the Fog

Setting the Stage:

It is a foggy morning as you drive down the highway. All your eyes can see is the road directly in front of you. Correlate this with your intention for your practice today; all you can see, breathe, and feel is your intention. Everything else is covered with fog. Breathe in your intention on a long inhale, pause, and slowly breathe out. As you continue to go up and down hills, around curves, and straight forward on your path, the intention is all you see.

Ever so slowly, the fog in your peripheral vision starts to lift. Begin to see the grass, trees, crops, and homes alongside the road, but your focus remains straight ahead. You can view the big picture now, but you're not distracted. All that matters is the road in front of you.

Use this as an analogy for your practice today. Your practice is centered on your intention; everything else is hidden by the fog. Even as the fog lifts, your body, mind, and soul remain focused on your intention. There are always distractions, but your focus is more powerful than the distractions.

As you begin to move through your poses, see only your intention on the road before you, consolidating with your breath and movement. Leave the rest in the fog.

Connecting throughout your practice:

On your inhale, there's a thick fog and you see only your intention, on the exhale, the fog lifts, but you remain focused on your intention

In balance poses, focus your drishti, or gaze, on a spot in front of you. Even though you're aware of the room and people around you, it's as if they're hidden in fog and you see only your focal point, allowing you to remain balanced.

Concentrate on a specific part of the body in your pose. Other parts that are also working and still others are relaxed, but it's as if they're covered in fog. Commit to focus on that one part, feeding its strength and engagement as it empowers you.

Examples:

Warrior II (Virabhadrasana II)

Look over your front fingertips as if all you can see is the road in front of you, and everything in your peripheral vision is covered with fog. Sink into your front knee, seeing only your intention beyond your fingertips. You're aware of other body parts working, your back leg is active as the back foot pushed down, hips are pushing toward the midline of your body, arms are extended, you feel and see these parts of the pose peripherally, but you remain strong in your intention gazing out over your front fingertips, softening your facial muscles.

King of the Dancers Pose (Natarajasana)

Establish your gaze and become aware of the leg that will be your standing leg. Shift most of your weight to this leg. Feel the big toe push into the mat, the even distribution of the weight on your foot, the calf engagement, and then the quad, and up into your strong core. This is your focus, what you see and feel strongly through the fog. As you add the other elements of the pose; reaching for the foot, tipping forward, raising your opposite arm to the side, thumb up; you don't become distracted; they naturally flow as you remain focused on the key elements. Your mind is focused on your intention through the fog, represented by the strength of the standing leg lifting up into the core.

Your turn: Choose some of the key poses that are part of your practice today. In a notebook, write specifically the words you would use to help your students utilize this visualization to enhance the pose and focus the mind.

Closing:

In savasana, gently close your eyes or look down at the tip of your nose. See that foggy road again, with the clear path straight in front of you filled with your personal intention. You might be aware of noises in the room or outside, or perhaps a worry or distraction floats into your mind. Simply let these drift off into the fog, allowing your mind and body to be filled solely with your intention. Be present in the quiet for the next few moments.

Before opening your eyes, take a moment to commit to remaining focused today. See yourself going through your day maintaining focus on what matters most. There will be other things to do, people who want something, challenges, distractions, and celebrations. Acknowledge them, but if they threaten your focus, simply visualize them drifting off into the fog. Your intention is clear.

Begin to awaken your body [cues]...

Booster:

I am committed and focused on my intention; I can let distractions drift into the fog.

Namaste

Variations:

The fog could be across the water, on a path, or walking down a sidewalk.

Visualize the fog in your mind, then lifting it and feeling a lightness.

Setting the Stage:

Choose a scent that's pleasing to you. This might be a scent from nature, such as fresh rainfall, or a flower. It could be a favorite spice, or the aroma of a favorite dish cooking; maybe it's an essential oil. Whatever it is, imagine you have a small bottle holding the scent. Gradually start to unscrew the lid, slowly lifting it off the bottle and moving your nose toward it. Inhale and fill your lungs with the pleasing aroma, and exhale as the corners of your mouth turn up in appreciations of this pleasing scent. [Pause] Decide on your intention for today, which could be a word or phrase such as peace, harmony, or letting go. Take a few more breaths and wrap the scent all around your intention, so that when you smell the scent you're reminded of the intention, and when you think of the intention, the scent enters your consciousness as well.

Become aware of the continuum of the scent you have selected. Bring into focus the slightest hint of that scent. On an inhale, gradually allow it to intensify, making it stronger, along a continuum, until you get to the strongest version of the scent that's still pleasing to you. It's not overpowering but encompassing. Fill your thoughts, mind, and breath with it. As you exhale, gradually bring it back down the continuum to its softest scent, where you're barely able to catch a faint essence.

We will use this today in our practice. During our strongest poses, the scent will be its strongest, reminding us of the strength of our intention. As we breathe into the pose or engage in relaxing poses, the scent will travel down the continuum in intensity. The softest version of the scent will drift to us when we are in a relaxed state, barely entering our awareness.

Connecting throughout your practice:

On an inhale, breathe in the scent, and, thus, your intention. On an exhale, allow the scent to become softer and your intention to fill the air around you. (Or, fill your body)

Contract your muscles and absorb the aroma in one of its stronger states; release your muscles and gradually, the scent becomes softer.

When flowing in poses, alternate the strong and soft versions. For example, bend and straighten your leg while preparing for Warrior II. Inhale a strong scent when straight, exhale, allowing it to become softer as you bend your knee and sink into the pose.

Examples:

Warrior II (Virabhadrasana II)

Feel the strength of your total core (navel, hips, lower back, sacrum) and the scent is powerful there. Your arms extend with power, yet a soft scent surrounds the shoulder blades as you relax them away from your ears, and still a softer version around your face where each muscle relaxes.

Eagle Pose (Garudasana)

A strong version of the scent fills your consciousness as you feel the strength in the standing leg, around your core, inner thighs, and arms as you press the limbs together. A very slight scent is present in the face as you release your forehead, jaw, and mouth.

Your turn: Choose some of the key poses that are part of your practice today. In a notebook, write specifically the words you would use to help your students utilize this visualization to enhance the pose and focus the mind.

Closing:

Coming into savasana, gently close your eyes or look down at the tip of your nose. Let your breath slow into a relaxing breath. An imaginary ball of a faint version of your scent is drifting a few inches above your face, still intertwined with your intention. As it pauses there, feel its energy loosening the muscles in your forehead, jaw, mouth, and lips. Now let the ball travel slowly down your body, pausing next at your neck and shoulders. The aroma and intention work together to relax these muscles and fill your being. The ball continues to travel down your torso, pausing over each section to release any bits of tension. If a certain part of your body still feels tight, imagine the scent getting a little stronger, then bring it back down the continuum to help it relax. Continue down your body. [Pause]. When you're finished, let the scent drift in and out of your awareness and allow your body to float in silence for a few moments, reveling in stillness.

[Pause]

Before coming out of your resting pose, commit to bringing your intention with you after you leave this practice. The scent can remind you of the intention, and the intention can be reinforced by the scent. If you feel stress, or the opposite of your intention during the day, bring to mind a strong version of the scent, and walk it down its continuum to visualize reducing the stressor.

Begin to awaken your body [cues]...

Booster:

I control my breath, focus, and state of being.

Namaste

Self-Acceptance & Confidence

If your compassion doesn't include yourself, it is incomplete.

–Buddha

Clouds of Confidence

Setting the Stage:

Take a moment to look up at the sky in daylight. Visualize when the sky is completely blue for endless miles, just as some days you feel unwavering strength and confidence. Visualize the times when there are a few white clouds interrupting the complete blueness, representing times when you have a few doubts in yourself, but can work through them and retain feelings of empowerment and confidence. Still other times, the white clouds move in and cover most of the sky, leaving only glimpses of blue. These are similar to times you feel lots of doubt but can cling to the splotches of blue hope. You may not feel strong, yet you know that strength is there. And other days, the sky is completely overcast representing when you're overcome with doubt; your confidence is shaky and challenged and all you can do is hang onto the belief that the blue is under the dark clouds.

Consider which type of sky you're under today, not in a judgmental way, but with acknowledgement. All the types of sky occur naturally, and they're all temporary. As the sky can change in a matter of minutes, so can your state of being. Accept where you are now, visualizing the sky that represents it and knowing it's natural and necessary. [Pause]

As you go through your practice today, acknowledge and accept the strengths and challenges in your body, just as you accepted your state of being as represented by the sky.

Connecting throughout your practice:

On an inhale, breathe in strength and confidence [or whatever intention that you need today]. On the exhale, blow away the clouds of doubt, or other obstacles that are in your way. This increases the amount of blue sky, symbolizing more confidence and strength in yourself.

When contracting your muscles, let the clouds swirl around in protest. On the release, the clouds dissipate, revealing more blue sky.

Examples:

Warrior II (Virabhadrasana II)

Stand confidently in Warrior II. Breathing deep into your core, your strength keeps the clouds from penetrating, and looking over your fingertips, there's blue sky. Look forward confidently at the blue sky and feel your unwavering strength as a warrior.

Boat (Navasana)

[Recommended Breath of Fire]

Sitting in boat pose, practice the breath of fire. Inhale your belief in yourself, on the short, quick exhales, the clouds swirl around in front of you and then drift off. This leaves space on your next inhale for the intake of even more confidence, and the pattern continues with each round of breath of fire.

Your turn: Choose some of the key poses that are part of your practice today. In a notebook, write specifically the

words you would use to help your students utilize this visualization to enhance the pose and focus the mind.

Closing:

Relax in savasana, imaging yourself on a soft, grassy knoll. Above you, notice how the sky has evolved from how it looked at the beginning of the practice. Appreciate the differences. How have you changed since your first pose? What's the same? What's different? What caused these changes? Again, appreciate the changes. Take a few moments to lose yourself peacefully in the sky, letting thoughts come and go just as the clouds come and go across the sky.

Before you awaken, commit to what you'll take with you today. How will you keep clouds from taking over your blue sky? When doubt or worry enter your mind, visualize the blue sky. You're strong. You're confident.

Begin to awaken your body [cues]...

Booster:

I can acknowledge my doubts, and, at the same time, know that I am strong and confident. I choose to feel confident.

Namaste

Your Extraordinary Self

Setting the Stage:

The dictionary defines the word "extraordinary" as "very unusual or remarkable" With your eyes closed or looking down at the tip of your nose, visualize some places or events that you would describe as extraordinary: maybe the ocean, a mountain, a beautiful butterfly, running a marathon, a graduation. Close your eyes and bring to mind the details of these images. What makes them extraordinary, or different from the ordinary in a positive way? Let the images and rationales flow through your mind. [pause]

Now call to mind some people whom you consider to be extraordinary. What makes them remarkable? What character traits or accomplishments do they possess? Let these flow in and out of your mind for a few breaths. [pause]

In today's practice, we'll focus on the word "extraordinary," specifically our extraordinary selves. Yes, we are each remarkable in our own way, we each have our own gifts to share. With each inhale, breathe in the belief that "I am extraordinary." On each exhale, let go of doubt. Make sure to empty your lungs, so that there's no room for doubt. Continue to take some balanced breaths, inhaling your extraordinary traits and letting go of everything that's the opposite. Repeat the mantra "I am extraordinary" throughout, until doubts disappear and your belief in your own state of extraordinary runs through you and around you…[Pause]

Open your eyes and focus your gaze on a place straight ahead at eye level or slightly above, see the image of "the extraordinary" or the mantra "I am extraordinary." As we begin to flow through poses, let this focal point remind you how extraordinary you are.

Connection throughout your practice:

Inhale to breathe in and remind yourself of one thing that's extraordinary about yourself, exhale to bring it (Choose 1)

- Through your body (name specific flow, throat, chest, ribs, abdomen, etc.)
- Into the muscle or body part(s) that are strongly engaged. Feel the strength of your uniqueness in the power of the pose
- Into the air or space around you, surrounding yourself with a remarkable sensation

Specific poses: During the peak of your pose, when you've landed your personal full expression of the pose, repeat the mantra "I am extraordinary."

Warrior II (Virabhadrasana II)

Gaze beyond your front fingers at your focal point and repeat the words "I am extraordinary" firmly and confidently, like a warrior. Slow the phrase down so you are saying only one word with each full breath.

Child's pose (Balasana)

As you relax deeply into child's pose, feel the extraordinary sensations in your lower back, side body, and shoulder blades.

Your turn: Choose some of the key poses that are part of your practice today. In a notebook, write specifically the words you would use to help your students utilize this visualization to enhance the pose and focus the mind.

Closing:

Relax in savasana, basking in the extraordinary differences in your body and mind. Physically, what parts of your body or muscle groups feel lengthened? Released? Relaxed? [Pause] Mentally, appreciate the extraordinary sense of accomplishment, focus, or other shift you have experienced during your practice. [Pause] Revel in these sensations, perhaps turning the corners of your mouth slightly upward in gratitude. Give yourself a few moments in the stillness to accept and appreciate these changes. [Pause]

Gradually return to the room around you, blinking your eyes and awakening your body. The reality of being an extraordinary person exists beyond this space and practice. It's a part of you, an unforgettable aspect of who you are. Commit to share your extraordinary self with others, to let yourself shine to those around you.

Namaste

Booster:

I believe in my extraordinary self.

Variations:

During the introduction, ask students to attach one of the extraordinary images to the mantra "I am extraordinary." Guide them in sensory details of what it looks like, sounds they hear, smells, and what they feel, as they continue to repeat the mantra. An image coupled with the mantra will assist in retrieving the belief during stressful times because there are more neural pathways with which to access it.

Majestic Mountain

Setting the Stage:

Begin in mountain [Tadasana] pose. Gently close your eyes or look down at the tip of your nose. As you inhale and exhale long breaths in and out your nose, feel the strength of your body rising up from your feet, and the strength of your mind, focused and clear. Identify your intention for your practice, breathing it up into your body and mind, and feeling its strength flow down throughout your body.

Be a mountain of strength in the intention you have chosen.

At the base of your mountain are the waves of the ocean. Feel the coolness of the water and hear the lapping sounds. At times, the waves are gentle and relaxing, barely touching your base. On other occasions, they're more turbulent, hitting against you with more force. Yet you remain strong. Sometimes the waves rise ferociously to your shins, your waist, and even your chest. But they don't knock you over.

Eventually, the turbulent waters pass, and the gentle waves again lap at your base. There may be changes to the mountain's surface, but not to the core. It's similar with yourself: Turbulence might cause changes, but you're strong in yourself, your intention, in all that's at the center of you.

Use this as an analogy during our practice today. In life, there may be times of calm waves and turbulent waves and every degree in between, but you're still the same majestic mountain.

Your core remains strong, unwavering, and firm in your intention.

Blink your eyes open and closed a few times, taking a moment to feel stable in mountain pose.

Connecting throughout your practice:

Applicable to all standing poses: Feeling strong through your core, feel the wave lapping at your base, sometimes gently, sometimes strongly, but remain firm and strong.

In seated poses, let the base of the mountain be where your bottom contacts the floor, tucking your sacrum and allowing the torso to rise firmly from your core. Ocean waves may try to lift one side of the body or the other off the floor but remain firmly planted.

Inhale, feel the height of the mountain; exhale to appreciate all that comprises the surface of the mountain (grass, trees, rocks, etc.).

Examples:

Warrior II (Virabhadrasana II)

Your front and back feet are the base of your mountain, feel the waves trying to disrupt the strength at your base. Remain grounded and confident through your core as you breathe with unwavering focus on your intention.

Tree Pose (Vrksasana)

Begin in tree pose with arms in prayer:

The foot connected with the floor forms a narrow, but rooted and unwavering mountain. When you're ready, take your arms to the tree position of your choice, keeping your gaze focused and core firm. Settle into tree pose. Feel the waves lapping at your narrow but strong base, sometimes calmly, sometimes with more force, but it's as if they're removed from you. You remain strong and firmly planted.

Your turn: Choose some of the key poses that are part of your practice today. In a notebook, write specifically the words you would use to help your students utilize this visualization to enhance the pose and focus the mind.

Closing:

As you come into savasana, allow the parts of your body touching your mat to be the base of your mountain. The more you melt into your mat and let go, the stronger the mountain becomes as you're one with the earth. Imagine the shoulder blades liquifying and move down your body to the back of your arms, chest muscles, lower back, gluts, thighs, calves, and heels (say each body part slowly, with at least a breath for each part). With each long breath, feel your body dissolve a fraction more. At your core, you're the unchanged mountain, the waves have modified your surface in some ways, but the core, whatever that is for you, is constant. Take a few minutes to allow your mind to be quiet and appreciate your core of strength.

Before you open your eyes, identify one trait about yourself that you acknowledge is unwavering within you. See yourself going through your day, keeping this piece of you as a resistance to the waves. Commit to yourself that the waves of the day, tasks, distractions, worries, will not erode your core of your intention.

Begin to awaken your body [cues]...

Namaste

Booster:

While I may be faced with turbulence, my core remains unwavering.

Recipe

Setting the Stage:

Gather the ingredients for one of your favorite recipes, maybe a cake or some cookies, anything that's pleasing to you. Set them on the counter and get everything else you'll need to make the recipe: bowls, spoons, and a pan. Looking at them, you wonder how some of the ingredients can create something tasty, for example, the flour. Alone, it doesn't taste good; it takes all of the other ingredients working together to make it into something yummy. And it has a purpose; without the flour, the cookies would be a runny mess, and definitely wouldn't be cookies.

Use this analogy for your practice and your life today. Each pose involves many parts of your body working together to create it. Some may be minor, such as the baking soda, but without it, the pose isn't complete, and could even cause harm. There might be favorite and less favorite poses, yet each has a purpose. And the same is true of life; there are so many experiences that come together to form you, some are less important and some more so, and some you might not like as much. Yet, all are necessary and come together to create the uniquely fascinating, essential person that's you.

Throughout our practice today, we'll be using this analogy to create strong, meaningful poses, important to our well-being. Just as in our lives, our experiences have created and continue to create a meaningful, essential, and balanced individual.

Connecting throughout your practice:

Inhale, see the individual ingredients gathered in your kitchen; exhale, call to mind the finished, tasty product that makes your mouth water and bursts with flavor with each bite.

As thoughts or worries creep into your mind, swirl them together to create the tasty favorite you enjoy so much. If they're not an ingredient for this recipe, gently put them back in the cupboard or refrigerator where they belong.

Contract your muscles to visualize an ingredient; release and appreciate the final product.

Examples:

Warrior II (Virabhadrasana II)

After settling into the pose, hold for 5-8 breaths. Appreciate how each ingredient-the engagement of the inner thighs pushing toward your midline, the even distribution of your weight in both feet, the buoyancy but firmness of your arms, your gaze over your front fingertips- comes together to make you a strong, confident, brave Warrior, a person of integrity, in your life. As is necessary for a Warrior, you're fully engaged and grounded.

Camel (Ustrasana)

Kneeling tall, put the ingredients of the pose together. Two hips are directly over your knees, one sacrum is tucked, one belly button is pushed back toward your spine to engage the core. Stir the ingredients, allowing your two hips and one abdomen to push forward. One chest is open, one neck is aligned, two hands reach back for the tops of two feet. All these ingredients come together to open your shoulders, heart, and mind.

Modification: (half camel): sometimes, it's necessary, based on your ingredients on hand, to make a smaller amount of your recipe, and some days, it's necessary to listen to your body and make a choice that's right for you, such as half camel. Slowly raise both hands to the sky, then pushing your abdomen forward, rotate your right hand down to your right heel. Keep the belly button facing forward, stretch the fingertips of the left arm to the ceiling, turning your face to gaze toward the left arm. Hold for a few breaths, then slowly release each element and move to the other side.

Your turn: Choose some of the key poses that are part of your practice today. In a notebook, write specifically the words you would use to help your students utilize this visualization to enhance the pose and focus the mind.

Closing:

As you rest in savasana, take a moment to appreciate how your body and your mind have changed since the beginning of the practice. Where are you more open, stronger, or more relaxed? Where is there still work to be done? If you're holding tension somewhere, focus on that place. Take several breaths, making a mind-body connection into the tension to release and relax it. The poses, your breath, your intention are all necessary ingredients that come together to create your current state of being. Pause and cherish how everything came together and improved your being, physically, mentally, and emotionally. [Pause]

Before you come out of your resting pose, consider how this applies to your life. All the pieces, even the least favorite, are necessary, just as you are necessary. You bring something to this earth, to the people in your life, to your job, that no one else can bring. Your being is valued, important, and necessary. Treasure and appreciate yourself.

Begin to awaken your body [cues]...

Namaste

Booster:

I trust all the ingredients in my being and my life to mix together for a purpose.

Gratitude

Gratitude makes sense of our past, brings peace for today, and creates a vision for tomorrow.

–Melodie Beattie

Star Gazing

Setting the Stage:

Gently close your eyes or look down at the tip of your nose. In your mind, let the darkness created by closing your eyes transform into the night sky, filled with zillions of stars. They extend as far and as deep as you can see. Take some slow, deep breaths in and out your nose as you appreciate the vastness.

Find a group of stars that fit together in a manner that makes sense to you. In your mind, draw a circle around that group. Focus on one star individually and name something you're grateful for today [offer suggestions if you feel like your class needs it: being here, breath, the sun or rain, etc.]. Inhale and exhale, centering on that star. Now move to the next star in the group, directing your mind and breath on something else for which you're thankful. Continue this with each star in your "group," naming something for which you're grateful and allowing at least one inhale and exhale on each. [Pause]

You're beginning to feel lighter and more energized. Draw a circle around another group of stars and repeat this process. [Pause]

Notice how much easier it is to identify what you're grateful for the more you do this, and that your mind is increasing in focus and positivity. Gratitude breeds gratitude, in your practice, and in your life.

When you're ready, gently open your eyes and come back to this physical space. Appreciate the differences in your breath, attitude, and body that have already occurred in this short time. As we go into our asanas or poses, be aware of the power of gratitude in your body and mind.

Connecting throughout your practice:

On the inhale, breathe in gratitude; exhale the energy of gratitude into [name a specific muscle that's a part of your pose]

Contract your muscles and visualize a specific star; release and fit it into the overall picture of the night sky.

On an inhale, breathe gratitude into your body; exhale to share gratitude with the world around you.

Examples:

Warrior II (Virabhadrasana II)

Looking out over your front fingertips, see the night sky filled with stars. On each star, place an image or word of something for which you're grateful

Child's Pose (Balasana)

Inhale the energy and lightness of gratitude; exhale into your low back and glutes, allowing the energy to release any tension. Repeat, releasing more tension each time.

Your turn: Choose some of the key poses that are part of your practice today. In a notebook, write specifically the

words you would use to help your students utilize this visualization to enhance the pose and focus the mind.

Closing:

As you move into savasana, gently close your eyes or find a focal point level with your eyes. Look up into a star-filled night sky once again and take a cleansing breath in the nose and out the mouth in appreciation. As you continue with either a balanced or relaxed breath through your nose, let your gaze float around the night sky, filling you with a sense of peace. Gradually, the stars start to fade, until they dim completely, and the sky is completely dark. The stars are gone, but the sense of gratitude and well-being remain. [Pause]

Before you come back to the room, commit to being filled with gratitude today. Keep a mental picture of the stars in the sky to remind you to remain positive.

As you go through your day, and challenges or hurries arise, focus your attention on what you've chosen and feel the power of gratitude work within you. Gratitude breeds gratitude.

Begin to awaken your body [cues]...

Namaste

Booster:

As the stars lighten the night sky, so gratitude lightens my being.

Variations:

Start with an empty night sky, and one by one with each breath, add a star to the sky by identifying something for which you're grateful. Soon, the sky is full of stars, and you feel light and energized.

Grasslands of Gratitude

Setting the Stage:

Envision yourself in a field of thick, soft, green grass. Feel the cool dampness on your feet and appreciate the lush greenness that has had the perfect amount of rain to maximize its vibrancy. Sitting down on the softness, ever so gently, rub a blade of grass between your fingertips, noting its soft, smooth texture. Gazing at it between your fingers, call to mind something for which you're grateful. Letting go of this blade, reach out for another blade of grass, remembering something else for which you're thankful. Release this piece, moving to another and another, and, just as each blade is a little different, you're able to name a unique item of gratitude for each blade you touch. [Pause]

Lift your head and look out over the vastness of the field, realizing you have as much to be grateful for as the limitless blades of grass your eyes behold. When you choose to focus on the thick, soft grass, the gratitude flows freely and brings you peace. Sometimes, however, you choose to focus on the sparse, prickly grass, where you find less for to be grateful for, and peace is harder to find. Today, focus on the lush, thick grass, and the plethora of blessings that fill your life.

Returning to stand, we root our feet down firmly in mountain pose, the softness of the grass under our toes reminding us to be grateful. Feel the energy of gratitude rise up your legs into your calves, knees, quads, tucking the sacrum under and rising up through your torso, neck, and going out through the crown of your head. Your body is filled with thankfulness, making you feel free and light.

As you start to move…

Connecting throughout your practice:

On an inhale, fill your body and mind with gratitude. On the exhale, see the breeze gently blowing the tips of the grass, causing gratitude to spread everywhere.

Let your body be long like a tall blade of grass nurtured with gratitude, as your body shortens, let the gratitude spread throughout the room, to others, and beyond.

Examples:

Warrior II (Virabhadrasana II)

Looking out over your front fingertips, conjure up once more the field of vibrant green, gently blowing in the breeze. Appreciate how gratitude is everywhere for as far as you can see, spreading further in the breeze. Feel its softness in your feet as you press both feet firmly in your warrior pose, allowing the abundance of gratitude to strengthen your pose and your mind.

Cat and Cow (Bidalasana)

On an inhale, look up and envision a field of gratefulness; on an exhale, round your spine, drop your head, and look behind you, noting that gratitude is there as well. It seems to be everywhere when you look for it.

Your turn: Choose some of the key poses that are part of your practice today. In a notebook, write specifically the words you would use to help your students utilize this visualization to enhance the pose and focus the mind.

Closing:

As you relax into savasana, let your body release into the mat. On each part of your body that touches the floor, feel the softness of the grass filling your body and soul with gratitude. This awareness further relaxes muscles on the front side of your body, allowing you to melt deeper into your mat and into a sense of gratitude. Close your eyes or look down at the tip of your nose, and rest for a few minutes in the stillness. If something tries to distract you, see it, and then let it blow softly across the field on the tips of the grass until gratitude absorbs it and it's no longer there.

[Pause]

Before you awaken, commit to being grateful today, fully appreciating how it makes your day flow easier.

Begin to awaken your body [cues]...

Namaste

Booster:

I choose gratitude, and the more I choose gratitude, the more there is to be grateful for.

Variations:

Envision gently pulling a blade of grass out of the ground without breaking it. From its white root to the greenness of its tip, see gratitude from where it's typically not visible in the ground or your root, to where it's visible at the tip, where all can see, and not only benefit from its presence, but spread to all.

Waterfall of Gratitude

Setting the Stage:

Envision a waterfall cascading between two large boulders. The power of the falls is awe-inspiring; take a moment to appreciate the feel of mist on your face, the cool dampness of the air, and the fresh scent of nature. Take a cleansing breath, in your nose and out your mouth.

The strong waterfall is a reminder of the numerous blessings in your life. Take a few moments to recall some of them to mind [here you could name some: your breath, the movement of your body, family members, the sunshine, the rain, your practice, being here]. Just as there are too many droplets of water to count, there are so many blessings for you to appreciate. The magnitude of them is overpowering, as is the force of water as it gushes to the pool below. It's inconceivable to stop the flow of water, and it's equally challenging to cease being grateful once you begin. [Again, you could name a few or let them think in silence-how much your breath has already slowed in the last few minutes, safe travels to this spot, someone holding the door for you, having enough to eat].

As you go through your practice today, pause to appreciate the power of a grateful mind and the strength it brings to you, similar to the strength of the waterfall. Sometimes the power seems lost to you, just as a waterfall may lose some of its strength during a drought. But when you fuel the fall with more water, it increases in strength again. Similarly, when you notice more abundance than shortages, gratitude becomes stronger and easier to find.

As you stand in mountain pose, feel a sense of gratitude for your feet rooting into the ground, the soft bend in your knees, the strength in your quads, the firmness of your core as your belly button presses back towards your spine, your shoulders down and back, and your head resting on top of your spine. Right here, in this stance, there's so much to appreciate in your body. As we continue through our poses, bring that sense of appreciation to each movement.

Connecting throughout your practice:

On the inhale, we'll bring the power of the falls and gratitude into our bodies. On the exhale, let the strength flow freely through your body.

When you contract your muscles, imagine the power of the falls concentrated in the muscle you're contracting. When you release the muscles, let it all go like the water flowing freely to the bottom.

Examples:

Warrior II (Virabhadrasana II)

As you gaze over your front fingertips, it's as if there's a slideshow playing of all the items for which you're grateful. Hold for five to seven breaths, envisioning people, traits, and experiences for which you are grateful pass through your field of sight.

Goddess (Utkata Konasana)

When you're settled in Goddess pose, turn your face upward. Imagine a waterfall of gratitude pouring over you, flowing deep into your body and mind.

Your turn: Choose some of the key poses that are part of your practice today. In a notebook, write specifically the words you would use to help your students utilize this visualization to enhance the pose and focus the mind.

Closing:

As you relax in savasana, gently close your eyes or softly gaze at the tip of your nose. Bring to mind that waterfall and fix your drishti, or gaze, on it, allowing it to mesmerize and relax each part of your body (you might choose to slowly name parts from head to toe: forehead, neck, shoulders, etc.). As you continue taking slow deep breaths, make a shift from being captivated by the water to being mesmerized by all you're grateful for. This state of being relaxes your body, and you melt into your mat with a strong feeling of "all is well." Relax in the stillness, resting in appreciation. [Pause]

Before you come out of your resting pose, commit to the power of gratitude somewhere in your life today. If you're worried about money, be grateful for the material comforts you do have. If you're concerned about a loved one, be grateful they're in your life. If you're worried about getting things done, be grateful you have tasks to do. Then notice how gratitude flows as strong and free as a waterfall...

Begin to awaken your body [cues]...

Namaste

Booster:

The power of gratitude washes away negativity and refreshes my being.

Variations:

Other cues might be that some days, the waterfall may be stronger or weaker; sometimes, the sense of gratitude is stronger or weaker, but it's still present.

Instead of a big waterfall, imagine a smaller one that trickles down a bank or stream. The water is still flowing, stronger than what it encounters (rocks, branches, debris), just as gratitude is stronger than negativity.

Sometimes, there's a drought and the waterfall ceases. Sometimes, we don't feel grateful, or like there's nothing to be grateful for. We must have patience and believe it will rain again and the waterfall will flow. We must also make a concerted effort to be grateful, and the strength of gratitude will return.

The waterfall visualization may be used to reinforce any intention, not only gratitude. Feel the strength of the water and correlate it with peace, breath, stability, harmony, or simply "your intention," which could be different for everyone. Like the droplets of water, the presence of the "intention" is too numerous to count.

Seeds of Gratitude

Setting the Stage:

Consider one popcorn seed: smooth, tiny, pointy, and brownish orange in color. Assign it something you're grateful for and place it into the popcorn kettle. Take another seed, name another item of gratitude, and put that one in the kettle as well. Keep doing this for a few more seeds, one breath and one seed at a time, noticing that as you go it's getting easier and easier to think of things for which you're grateful. [Pause]. Noticing how gratitude breeds gratitude, look at the remaining seeds in your cup, knowing you have at least that many reasons to be grateful, and pour it all into the heating kettle.

All of the seeds of gratitude mix together, swirling around as they heat up. Pop...pop...pop! Gratitude cannot be contained, and it spills over out of the pot, and into all areas of your life. Slowly at first, then picks up speed; pop, pop, pop. The more you focus on what you're grateful for, the more the energy builds, and expands your thoughts, feelings, attitude, and action into full kernels of gratitude.

As you go through your practice today, hear the sound of the popcorn, smell its aroma, envision it spilling from the kettle, and be reminded of gratitude.

Connecting throughout your practice:

Inhale and see the small seed of gratitude, exhale to experience the flow of positive energy that explodes and spreads to your body (or name a specific part) and all parts of your being.

Contract and feel the smoothness of the small popcorn seed; release as you feel the pressure pop into a fluffy kernel.

Examples:

Warrior II (Virbahadrasana II)

Stand firm in Warrior II, feeling the flow of energy throughout your body. Some parts are fully engaged, such as the inner thighs, quads, core, and torso. These are the seeds. Every part of your body is affected, and the firmness, engagement and energy of these parts pours into the rest of your body. The more seeds of gratitude you foster, the more gratitude provides energy and engagement in your life. Be strong like a Warrior in both your pose and in gratitude.

Seated Forward Bend (Paschimottanasana)

Inhale to breathe your arms up and long, filling your mind with gratitude, exhale to fold from your core as your torso pours over your legs and gratitude pours out of your beings. Inhale to a half lift with your hands on your shins (quads or ankles) filling up your lungs again, and exhale pour over your legs feeling the gratitude explode. Stay for several breaths, allowing the seeds of positive energy to fill your core, and gratitude to fill your mind and spirit.

Your turn: Choose some of the key poses that are part of your practice today. In a notebook, write specifically the words you would use to help your students utilize this visualization to enhance the pose and focus the mind.

Closing:

Resting in savasana, gently close your eyes or look down at the tip of your nose. Almost all of the popcorn seeds have popped into kernels, and you hear only a pop, pop every so often as the last few seeds explode. Look at the overflowing batch of white, fluffy kernels and smell its yummy aroma. It even feels different. Your mind has changed too; those little seeds of gratitude have expanded to fill your being with gratitude. Once it started, you couldn't stop it. And once you start focusing on gratitude, gratitude flows into every aspect of your life. Appreciate the changes in your body since we started, in your mind, and in your spirit. [Pause]

Before opening your eyes and awakening your body, commit to taking the kernels of gratitude with you to at least one area of your life. Be prepared to experience how the seeds of gratitude transform that area of your life, similar to how heat transforms a tiny seed into a white, fluffy kernel.

Begin to awaken your body [cues]...

Namaste

Booster:

Gratitude breeds gratitude. At this moment, I choose to be grateful.

Variations:

While this isn't necessarily a variation, it might be helpful to provide some suggestions of gratitude when setting the stage and throughout. Some suggestions include your breath, being here today, special people in your life, the sun, the rain (or whatever the current weather is), arriving here safely, confidence, faith, questions, opportunities, change, growth, and peace. Perhaps note that you might be working on developing more faith, peace, or other intention, but be grateful for how far you've come and how much of these qualities you already possess.

Letting Go

Some of us think holding on makes us strong, but sometimes it is letting go.

–Herman Hesse

Holding on is believing that there's only a past, letting go is knowing there's only a future.

–Daphne Rose Kingma

Setting the Stage:

Take a cleansing breath, in the nose and out the mouth. Begin to become more aware of your breath, not judging or trying to change it but noticing its rhythm and depth. Over the next few breaths, transition to allowing both the inhale and the exhale to flow through your nose. Finally, begin to balance your breath with an even count, taking a long inhale as you count 1, 2, 3, 4, 5, 6, hold for one count, and exhale 6, 5, 4, 3, 2, 1, and hold empty for one count. Repeat, being careful that it's one inhale with 6 counts (not 6 inhales) and one exhale to the count of 6 (or whatever count works for you). [Pause] After repeating several times, let go of the counting and more naturally keep your breath at an even pace. Notice changes that have happened already.

Envision yourself by a small body of water such as a pond or lake. You're comfortably seated or standing near the edge; pebbles and small rocks are on the ground. Take a moment to appreciate how the sun reflects off the weather, or if it's evening, how shadows stretch across the water. As you continue balanced breathing, close your eyes for a moment and listen to the sounds around you: the breeze, birds, and insects. And feel the coolness of the shade and the softness of the breeze.

Open your eyes and look out over the water. Pick up one of the rocks and consider one of your concerns or worries as you look at it, removing the concern from your mind and placing it within the rock. Calmly, and with determination, throw the rock into the water. As it sinks, watch the ripples surrounding it move further and further away, getting weaker the farther out they go, until eventually they disappear altogether. When you look back at where the rock was thrown, you see no evidence it was there. You've released this worry.

Pick up another pebble, and again, transfer a concern or negative thought to the rock. Throwing it into the water, watch the ripples get smaller and smaller until they diminish completely. You're freed from another thought that was working against you.

Repeat this process as many times as you need to, releasing a thought, concern, or challenge with each rock, and watching the ripples until they disappear along with the negative energy. Feel a bit lighter with each of them, as your mind is freed more with the release of each rock.

[Pause]. Your mind is now free, you're free to concentrate on your practice.

Connecting throughout your practice:

Inhale/Exhale: On the inhale, focus on the tight ripples around where the rock lands in the water, and on the exhale, follow the ripples until they disappear.

Contract and release: As you contract, focus on a thought concern or challenge, and as you release, watch the ripples until they disappear.

Parts of the body that are engaged most intensely are where the ripples are the tightest, less engaged parts are the smaller ripples further away. Another way to look at it would be when you take the first breath in the pose, the ripples are very tight, and as your muscles start to relax, the ripples get further apart until they disappear.

Examples:

Warrior II (Virbahadrasana II)

Sink into the pose, pausing to take at least 5 deep breaths.

Your first breath after sinking into the pose correlates to how close the ripples are together as the rock hits the water. With each breath, relax deeper into the pose, watching as the ripples get further and further apart, until they fade away completely.

Warrior II (Virbahadrasana II) with flow: bend and straighten the knee

On an inhale, straighten the leg as the rock contacts the water, exhale as you sink into a bent knee and the ripples move out over the water. Repeat for 3-5 breaths, then hold in Warrior II, feeling the tension let go as the ripples disappear.

Seated wide leg forward fold (Janu Sirsasana)

Inhale, turn your body toward the straight leg. Touch your palms over your head, exhale, extend, folding over the leg as the rock hits the water and sets the ripples into motion. With each breath, watch the ripples get smaller and smaller as you relax deeper and deeper into the fold.

Your turn: Choose some of the key poses that are part of your practice today. In a notebook, write specifically the words you would use to help your students utilize this visualization to enhance the pose and focus the mind.

Closing:

Gently close your eyes or look down at the tip of your nose. Take a cleansing breath in your nose, and out your mouth. Continue to breathe in your nose, and out your mouth, transitioning to a relaxing breath, where your inhale has twice as many counts as the exhale. As you breathe, scan your body and note any areas that are still tight. Focus on one area at a time, visualizing the ripples becoming further apart as you breathe into the muscle and the tension gradually let go until it's totally relaxed. Focus on the next area of tightness, releasing the tightness as the ripples move across the water. Continue until all tenseness has been relaxed in your body [Pause]

Allow yourself some time now to reflect on how your body felt at the beginning of your practice, and how it feels now. Appreciate the changes in your body, and the ripple effects of the changes on your mind and spirit. {Pause]

Begin to awaken your body [cues]...

Namaste

Booster:

Letting go of tension has positive ripple effects on my body, mind, and spirit.

Setting the Stage:

Take a deep cleansing breath in the nose and out the mouth. Gradually begin to shift your breath going in the nose and out the nose, increasing your awareness of your breathing and making it a little bit deeper. One possibility is a balanced breath, which means you count in for the same number on the inhale as you do on the exhale. You might inhale 1, 2, 3, 4, hold at the top feeling your lungs expand, and slowly exhale 4, 3, 2, 1, holding empty. Continue, counting for 6 to 8 on the inhale and exhaling the same number of counts. Remember, you're not inhaling 6 times; it's one inhale to the count of 6. After you've done this a few times, you won't need to count but be aware of how your breath has already changed in the past few minutes.

Become aware of the sounds around you as you begin walking along a wooded path carrying a heavy backpack. Listen to the birds, frogs, insects, or the rustle of the wind in the trees. Feel the coolness of the shade as you go further along the path. As you come around a bend, you arrive at a flat, grassy clearing. Walking to the center of the clearing, you see there's a wide, shallow hole and peer into it.

It occurs to you that you could leave some of your burden in the hole during your hike, and the idea of continuing without the extra weight energizes you. Slowly, you place all the things you don't need into the hole, including your anxieties, worries, to-do lists, and unrealistic expectations for yourself. A few times, you feel a tinge of guilt or panic, but you decide to leave the guilt and panic behind as well.

After you've unburdened yourself, continue around the hole to the other side where the path resumes. You feel much lighter as you proceed, breathing deeply and more aware of the sights, sounds, and smells. Coming around the next curve, you see that the path is surrounded by mini floral gardens of positive intentions: tranquility, peace, self-acceptance, balance, harmony. Visit the gardens that appeal to your needs. Stop to breathe in the intention, and on the exhale, allow it to fill your entire being. After a few deep breaths, place some in your backpack to take with you. It will be silent for a few moments now so you can visit the gardens of your choice, filling yourself with the intentions you need the most. [Pause]

Surprisingly, instead of weighing you down, the intentions seem to empower you to keep going. Feeling somehow lighter and stronger, round a bend and to the hole where you left your belongings. Still filled with lightness, carefully peer into the hole, aware of the need to claim your belongings but feeling oddly at peace with it. Carefully sift through what you left there, mindfully choosing what you take back, and how much. Some of it you choose because it's your responsibility, some of it because it's a part of you, and some because it's the right thing. But it's all a choice, and because of this, it's no longer weighing you down. The gifts from the various gardens you visited balance these things and continue to keep you light.

Return to where you began this journey, noticing and appreciating the differences in your being.

You're lighter, and you're filled with many gifts that are stronger than what once weighed you down. Give yourself permission to take what you've been offered on this journey with you, to let it be stronger than what was slowing you down earlier. Commit to yourself to allow your inspiration to be your focus, not taking away your challenges, but making your challenges only a piece of you instead of defining you.

As we begin to move through our poses, continue to feel light and energized.

Connecting throughout your practice:

Inhale those gifts from the garden, exhale, let them surround you.

Contract and release: Contract and feel the tension of the burdens; release and feel the light of the gifts (or of the inspiration). As poses are repeated or revisited, you notice there's less tightness as the burdens decrease.

Examples:

Warrior II (Virabhadrasana II)

Looking out over the front middle finger, fix your gaze on a focus point; the focus point is your intention. Take 5 deep breaths, and with each breath bring into focus more details of your intention.

Plank pose (Phalakasana)

Feel your hands and feet rooted in the ground; these are those gifts from the garden making everything possible. Your core, your midsection, your thighs are firmly part of you as are your challenges, but the tranquility, peace, and other gifts allow you to hold firm.

Your turn: Choose some of the key poses that are part of your practice today. In a notebook, write specifically the words you would use to help your students utilize this visualization to enhance the pose and focus the mind.

Closing:

Let your feet fall open, arms to your side. Close your eyes or look down at the tip of your nose. Take a cleansing breath in the nose and out the mouth, then return to a more natural balanced breath, or relaxing breath. Take a moment to appreciate your journey, both on the path and throughout your practice today. Your body and mind have been active, and now it's time to let them both relax.

Imagine a soft, warm light hovering over your face, relaxing your face muscles: eyes, cheeks, jaws, lips...the light now travels down your neck to your torso, easing out any remaining bits of tension and allowing your body to melt into the mat. [Slowly:] Ribs, abs and the entire core, hips, quads, knees, calves, feet out to the toes. Everything is relaxed and your breath is even; take a little time in silence to be in the moment.

Before awakening your body, commit to take with you some of the gifts you picked up along the path, whatever that was for you (peace, harmony, self-acceptance). Even though you have burdens, commit to the gifts easing your load and helping you feel light. See yourself moving through your day being light and focused on your intention.

Begin to awaken your body [cues]...

Namaste

Booster:

I choose what I take with me on my journey, and what I pick up along the way.

Variations:

Instead of a hole, travel on the path and when you come to a garden, realize you must leave something behind to accept the gift of that garden. Decide on something you don't need, perhaps a worry, leaving it and taking, instead, the gift of trust.

Instead of picking things up from the hole at the end, decide to leave them as you don't need them. You have everything you need.

Bridge

Setting the Stage:

Take a walk on a long bridge; whether it be a suspension bridge, covered bridge, arched bridge, or truss bridge, look forward. Notice the scenery surrounding the bridge; do you see water? Trees? Concrete? Is it quiet or loud? Is it still or packed with activity? Paint a picture in your mind with details: the colors, sounds, and energy. [Pause]

The bridge is taking you from where you've been to where you're going. You cannot see everything that's in front of you, but you can see your next step, so take one step at a time. If you turn your head and look over your shoulder, see where you've come from, but you're no longer there. It's a part of who you are, yet it's behind you now. Learn from it, let it go, and move forward.

As we move through our poses today, let go of tension and tightness in your body, and move forward into flexibility, looseness, and relaxation.

Connecting throughout your practice:

Inhale and consider what's in front of you, exhale to let go of what's behind.

In a particular pose, take stock of where you are TODAY. It doesn't matter what you could do yesterday, and maybe tomorrow will be different, but appreciate what's accessible to you today.

Examples:

Warrior II (Virabhadrasana II)

Check the alignment of your shoulders and arms by turning your neck and looking toward your back hand. Make any adjustments. Then, leave what's behind you in the past. Take stock of what each element of the pose right now, noting where there's tension, tightness, loosening, and relaxation. Finally, look over the front fingertips with a focused intention

Extended side angle (Utthita Parsvakonasana)

Feel one line of energy from the little toe side of your foot all the way out your top fingertips. The energy of what's behind you grounds you to the floor (past), affecting each part of you and building the energy and flow for what's happening now and moving forward.

Your turn: Choose some of the key poses that are part of your practice today. In a notebook, write specifically the words you would use to help your students utilize this visualization to enhance the pose and focus the mind.

Closing:

While in savasana, reflect on the changes that have occurred in your body, and in your mind since our first poses today. Appreciate the changes, both where you were at the start, or in your past, what has happened since, and where you are now, in the present. Letting go isn't always easy, moving forward is scary, so be in the moment. It's safe here. You're where you need to be. Take some time to accept this and be with yourself, right here, right now, you and your breath. Right here, right now, all is well. Melt into your mat, and breathe… [Pause 3-5 minutes]

Before awakening from savasana, take a moment and commit to letting go of what no longer serves you, looking forward to what lies ahead, and living in the present moment.

Begin to awaken your body [cues]...

Namaste

Booster:

I let go of the past, look forward to the future, and embrace the present. All are vital.

Variations:

The bridge could be a bridge from one version of a pose to either the next version or level. Some examples are:

Low lunge is a bridge to high lunge

Bridge pose is a bridge to wheel

Squat is a bridge to crow

Flames of Farewell

Setting the Stage:

Flames of orange and red dance before you. Pop, pop, crackle, crackle. Stare into the small fire and bring to mind your intention for today. See it in the flames as they move about, from the core of the fire to the wavering tips. [Pause]

Each obstacle to your intention is written down on a piece of paper. Carefully place the first one in the fire, watching the flame slowly curl the paper until it disappears completely, into the flame of your intention. Your intention is stronger than the obstacle. Slowly, place the next obstacle in the fire, watching as the flame engulfs it as well. Your intention is stronger than this obstacle. One by one, each obstacle burns, allowing the flame of your intention to overcome it. Continue until all the pieces of paper have been added to the fire. [pause]. It's only you and your intention now; Nothing is in the way.

As we move through our poses, remain focused on your intention. If a doubt or obstacle drifts into your mind, simply envision the flame engulfing it and return your focus to your intention.

Connecting throughout your practice:

Inhale your intention, exhale, breathe your intention out, allowing your breath to fuel the fire.

Envision the fire being strong and hottest in the part or parts of your body that are most engaged, less so in other parts.

Contract your muscles as you see the obstacle; release the muscles and let obstacle go into the flames

Examples:

Warrior II (Virabhadrasana II)

Sink into the front knee, feeling the fire burn strong in your core, the little toe side of your back foot, hip flexors, and front knee. As you look out over your front fingertips, envision your intention dancing in the fire.

Locust (Salabhasana)

Feel the fire of your intention flowing down the back of your body, from your upper spine, down to your glutes, hamstrings, and through your feet. The flames of your intention radiate off the back side of your body.

Your turn: Choose some of the key poses that are part of your practice today. In a notebook, write specifically the words you would use to help your students utilize this visualization to enhance the pose and focus the mind.

Closing:

As you come into savasana, gently close your eyes or look down at the tip of your nose. The flames are slowly fading, but the embers continue to burn strong. The crackle of those embers reminds you of your intention. Even though the flames have diminished, the intention is still as powerful as the embers, ready to spring to life if provoked by a doubt. Let your breath deepen as the fire fades, leaving you relaxed and melting into your mat, your mind drifting…[Pause]

Before opening your eyes, be aware that the physical fire was extinguished, but commit to keeping the flame of your intention with you when you leave this space. Your obstacles have been engulfed, you're strong in your intention and will remain strong as you participate fully in your life.

Begin to awaken your body [cues]...

Namaste

Booster:

My intention burns strong and can engulf any obstacle. I am powerful.

Relaxation

Your mind will answer most questions if you learn to relax and wait for the answer.

–William S. Burroughs

The time to relax is when you don't have time for it.

–Sydney J. Harris

Winding Down with the Wind

Setting the Stage:

Stand in your favorite outdoor space, closing your eyes and feeling the wind on your skin. Sometimes it's a soft breeze, barely registering in your consciousness; at other times, it's strong and powerful, and you stand firm in order not to lose your balance. Take a moment and feel the continuum of the wind, starting as a soft breeze, then gradually increasing little by little until it's at its most powerful force that's still refreshing and safe. Now, little by little, let the intensity of the wind decrease until it returns to the softest caress of a breeze.

The wind is doing an important job for you today; it's clearing your mind of distractions, worries, and stressors. Take an inhale focusing your mind on one specific distraction, worry, or stressor. On the exhale, let the wind carry it away, freeing your mind. Continue to breathe in and out your nose in a balanced style, inhaling to identify a specific distraction, and exhaling to release it in the wind. Sometimes, it gently floats away in the breeze; and other times, let a powerful gust carry it as far away from you as possible. In either case, the result is that your mind becomes freer and freer with each breath, until it feels completely clear and light.

Now that you've created space, choose an intention for your practice today. You're now free to focus on your practice and intention. If a thought, worry, or concern returns to distract you, acknowledge it and release it again in the wind, leaving your continued focus on your intention.

As you begin to move...

Connecting throughout your practice:

Focus on one specific stressor on the inhale; exhale and release the stressor to the wind.

Inhale to feel the crowdedness of your mind; exhale to release the crowd and relax.

Contract and feel the tension brought to your body; release and let a gentle breeze blow the tension away from your body.

Examples:

Warrior II (Virabhadrasana II)

Sink into your pose, remaining strong in the core, and allowing the wind to support your arms so they're firm but buoyant. As you focus your gaze over your front fingertips, the wind gently releases your facial muscles (forehead, cheekbones, jaw, tongue on roof of mouth). Your legs and core are firmly planted so that even the most powerful wind couldn't make them sway, yet your face muscles remain soft and your mind focused on your intention.

Breathing Bridge (Setu Bandha Sarvangasana)

Inhale, press the hips up and the hands overhead as the wind fills your mind, pushing away your thoughts; exhale, drop the arms by your side and your bottom to the ground, leaving your head clear and free with only enough space for your positive intention.

Reclined cobbler (Supta Baddha Konasana)

Place your hands in a diamond shape over your navel. Feel the steady rise and fall of your abdomen with the breath. As your belly rises on the inhale, your mind is filled with a gentle breeze, clearing your thoughts; as your belly falls on the exhale, your lungs and mind empty with only enough room for your intention.

Your turn: Choose some of the key poses that are part of your practice today. In a notebook, write specifically the words you would use to help your students utilize this visualization to enhance the pose and focus the mind.

Closing:

Lying in savasana, there's a light breeze floating over your face, blowing softly to relax each facial muscle. Feel the breeze flow down your body, softening each muscle into the mat along the way, [next parts slowly…] neck, shoulders, elbows, wrist, hands, fingers, chest, ribs, abdomen, hips, glutes, thighs, knees, calves, ankles, feet, toes, and then it drifts away. Every part of you has become so soft it has melded into one with the mat. The corners of your lips curve up in a soft smile; your body and mind are free of all tension and filled with your intention.

[Pause]

With your eyes still closed, commit to bringing this freeness of mind with you when leaving this space. When stressors enter your mind, let the breeze carry them away, leaving you solely with your intention.

Begin to awaken your body [cues]...

Namaste

Booster:

I choose where to focus my mind and release what isn't useful into the wind.

My Favorite Place

Setting the Stage:

Bring to mind a favorite place that offers peace and positivity.

Where are you?

Slowly call to your awareness details about this special place.

What do you see? [Slowly:] Colors, contrast, objects, lightness or darkness. Sharpen the image...Be present in this space.

What sounds do you hear? Loud or soft, high pitched or deep, background or forefront? Allow the sounds to come and go, not trying to figure them out or where they come from, just hearing them. Be present in this space

What smells are associated with this place? Are they strong, moderate, or weak? Constant or periodic? Singular or multiple? Bring it all into focus. Be present in this space.

What do you feel? Is it hot, warm, or cold? Smooth or rough? Soft or strong? Everywhere or localized to one spot? Be present in this space

Bring everything together to experience this special place. Why do you find it so comforting? What feelings connect with your images? As you breathe in and out, let the comfort of this place radiate within you and around you. [Pause]

As we go through our practice today and your mind wanders, or you feel challenged by a pose, bring your thoughts back to this place and focus on a small detail, whether it be a sight, sound, smell, or feeling, until you regain your focus and are present in this space.

Connecting throughout your practice:

Inhale to experience sight, sound, or feeling from your place; on the exhale, let the big picture come into focus.

When you contract your muscles, call to mind what you see, feel, or hear when you're about to arrive at your favorite place. Release and feel the comfort of having arrived.

Examples:

Warrior II (Virabhadrasana II)

With each round of breath, sink deeper into the details of your favorite place...sights…sounds...feelings…

AND/OR

As you look over your front fingertips, your vision and other senses are filled with your favorite place. See the image playing like a movie on your focal point and let the sense of comfort wash over you.

Knee-down twist (Supta Parivartanasana)

Settle into the twist, keeping your shoulders on the floor. Inhale and fill your senses with a detail of your favorite place; exhale and let the comfort of the place allow you to relax deeper into the pose.

Your turn: Choose some of the key poses that are part of your practice today. In a notebook, write specifically the

words you would use to help your students utilize this visualization to enhance the pose and focus the mind.

Closing:

As you come into savasana, take a cleansing breath in your nose and out your mouth. Slowly start to even out your breath and conjure up the images of that favorite spot one more time.

On your next complete breath, return to the sights: the colors, shapes, lighting, and small details.

In this next breath, return to the sounds: soft or loud, close and far away, essential and background…

Now focus on what you smell: slight or strong, pleasing or not so much, relaxing or energizing.

Finally, focus on what you feel; what sensations are happening on your face? What about your arms? Hands? What about the core? Traveling down to legs and feet.

It's time to leave your special place, but not the sense of comfort it brings you. The sights fade, the sounds dim, the scents drift away, but the healing presence of the place goes with you. It will be with you throughout the day, in chaotic times, busy times, quiet times, work times, and play times, because it's a part of you. A sight, a sound, a scent can conjure up this sense of comfort any time it's needed.

Begin to awaken your body [cues]...

Namaste

Booster:

Utilizing my senses allows me to be present in this space for this moment.

Melting into Mindfulness

Setting the Stage:

Start with your favorite relaxation breath for a few minutes. One suggestion is to inhale for a count comfortable to you, hold at the top with your lungs full, exhale for a count that's twice as long as your inhale, and hold your diaphragm empty for a count. [pause]

We are going to practice the sensation of letting our muscles melt in our practice today, so I would like you to call to mind an object of your choice that melts. Some possibilities are a candle melting into wax, ice cubes melting into water, butter changing from solid to liquid, chocolate, or even snow. Whatever that is for you, imagine it in the solid form on your body parts touching the mat as you inhale, exhale let it turn your muscles into liquid allowing them to melt into your mat. Take some time to start at the top of your body and use this process as you move down to contract and release the muscles. Inhale to use your neck muscles to push your head into the floor, visualizing your object in its solid form; exhale and see the element in its liquid form as your neck and head melt into the mat. Move next to your shoulders, pushing them into your mat on the inhale; exhale, allowing them to release and melt. Continue this process, sliding your shoulders up your mat to your ears on the inhale; exhale and slide them back down as the muscles liquify. It will be quiet now as you continue down your body, first tensing your muscles in a solid inhale, then letting them melt on the exhale. Hands, hips and glutes, quads, calves, ankles, and feet, pausing for a few breaths anywhere where you feel a greater amount of tension until every part of your body has melted into a pool of liquid. [Pause]

As we go through our relaxation poses, let this visualization work in your mind as well. When a thought or worry enters your consciousness, acknowledge its presence, then simply visualize it melting away, allowing your mind to be free.

Within the next couple of breaths, roll to your right side, then gradually come up to a seated, cross-legged pose.

Connecting throughout your practice:

Basically, this is a repeat of what was practiced while setting the stage, but in specific poses with targeted muscle groups.

Inhale to tense your muscles and envision the solid element, exhale to relax the muscles and allow them to melt to liquid.

Contract to envision the solid element, exhale to release and allow it to melt.

Face muscles: This will be part of the closing, but remind students to let their face muscles melt, especially in more challenging poses.

Examples:

Warrior II (Virabhadrasana II)

Settle into your pose, visualizing your hip flexors melting downward while still tracking your big toe on the inside of your bent knee. With each breath, allow the muscles to melt a little more, envisioning a slow melting of the wax, ice, or butter. Arms are firm, but melt your shoulder blades down your back to a consistency in between solid and liquid.

As you gaze over your front fingers, let your cheekbones and jaw melt, gently parting your lips to release those muscles.

Head to Knee (Janu Sirsasana)

Sit tall, turn toward your extended leg on the inhale, slowly exhale as you melt from the waist over that leg, stopping when your palms reach the floor. Inhale and solidify again lifting halfway to a straight spine, exhale to melt a little deeper as your hands walk forward toward your feet. When you get as far as you're going, take another inhale, this time allowing your shoulders, neck, and head to melt into the extended knee. Stay for 8-10 breaths, feeling your abdominal wall solidify a few degrees on the inhalations, and letting everything melt again on the exhalations

Your turn: Choose some of the key poses that are part of your practice today. In a notebook, write specifically the words you would use to help your students utilize this visualization to enhance the pose and focus the mind.

Closing:

Lie in savasana, taking a cleansing breath in your nose and out your mouth. Pause for a moment to notice any changes since we began our practice. Where are places in your body that are "solid," which places have melted, and which places are somewhere in between? Be careful not to judge but be aware.

Be present in the silence, returning to a relaxing breath in your nose and out your nose. If a thought pops into your mind, let it melt away. Slowly relax your face muscles, starting at your forehead, down your jaw and cheekbones; let your tongue touch the roof of your mouth, relaxing your lips. Let yourself be… [Pause]

Before you open your eyes, acknowledge that it's not feasible to go through your day in a melted pool, but neither is it necessary for our minds or bodies to be a solid mass of tension. Strive to recognize situations during the day when you become vulnerable to the extremes, whether it be a solid mass or a liquid pool, and commit to a balance between the two in your response, thoughts, and actions.

Begin to awaken your body [cues]...

Namaste

Booster:

I am in control of the amount of tension or relaxation I carry in my body.

Variations:

For consistency or with new students, choose a specific malleable item from the choices, and integrate that language specifically into the practice. For example, allow your hip flexor to go from a tense ice cube into a pool of water. Or as your neck relaxes, see the muscles go from a candle to melted wax.

River

Setting the Stage:

Imagine yourself by a flowing body of water: a river, stream, or creek. Watch the water as it flows smoothly. It doesn't stop for rocks, branches, or any other obstacle; it keeps flowing. Sometimes, it changes direction; sometimes, it slows down; and sometimes, it speeds up. But it's always flowing. At times, the water is turbulent, filled with current and swirls, and other times it's smooth, but it's always flowing. It doesn't know its direction, but it keeps flowing. Giving life, hosting life, interacting with life, powerful, and, at the same time, tranquil.

While we practice today, consider how you're similar to this body of water. There are often obstacles in your life, and you manage to either flow over them, or around them, or to change them. But you keep going. Sometimes, your life, emotions, or mental state is turbulent, swirling with uncertainty, doubt, or fear, and, at times, everything flows together peacefully. And you keep going. Sometimes, you don't know where you're going or why, what you're changing or how, but you keep going. You're strong, consistent, and powerful, and a wonder that draws people to be near you, admire you, and appreciate you.

Feel that strength rise through you as you open your eyes and begin the asanas. Your gaze or drishti is in this room physically, yet your mind sees and feels the flow of the river as we flow through our poses.

Connecting throughout your practice:

On an inhale, see the rushing power of the water; on an exhale, see its peaceful flow.

As you contract your muscles, see the water pool around an obstacle; as you release them, the water works its way free and continues its journey.

Your intention or purpose flows freely (through your body, mind, being), touching all as it continues to flow.

Examples:

Warrior dance (Virabhadrasana)

After the first dance cuing the physical aspects of the pose: flow through the poses, just as the river flows smoothly in its course. Breathe in, reaching back in Warrior I, feeling the power of the river's flow; exhale and sink into Warrior II. Inhale, continue the flow into reverse Warrior, and, with a surge of steady energy, exhale all the way forward into side-angle pose. As the river flows, you continue to flow, strong and consistent.

Yogi bicycle:

Let your moves flow smooth and consistent, inhaling long; exhale, crossing the elbow across your body while bringing the opposite knee in. Release long, switching sides and engaging the muscles, just as the river continues to engage no matter what the obstacles it encounters.

Your turn: Choose some of the key poses that are part of your practice today. In a notebook, write specifically the

words you would use to help your students utilize this visualization to enhance the pose and focus the mind.

Closing:

As you lie in savasana, let your mind flow with the river. Envision a ball of cleansing water above your face, gently pouring over your facial muscles, relaxing each one. The water source slowly travels down your body, releasing your neck muscles, your shoulders, gently flowing down your arms and washing away any remaining bits of tension in your elbows, wrists, palms, and fingers. It travels down your torso, gently easing each muscle into relaxation through your chest, abdomen, hips, and glutes. Let it all wash away as it continues down your thighs, kneecaps, calves, heel ankle, foot, and toes. You're now clean from tension, free from worries and thoughts, and feel as if you're floating on the water. Let your mind go, let your body go, and let yourself flow.

Before you open your eyes, take some time to appreciate the changes in your mind and body, and the cleansing power of water. Commit to an image that will remind you of your journey today and allow you to flow peacefully through your day.

Begin to awaken your body [cues]...

Booster:

I trust the flow of my life. I am where I need to be.

Namaste

Closing Message

Thank you for reading this book; more importantly, thank you for trying the visualizations personally or with your students. Today, life consists of so much stimulation and chaos. My wish is that you've found a tool that helps you deepen your yoga practice, resulting in a more purposeful and peaceful existence. I would love to hear from you: successes, challenges, questions, and comments. Please contact me at willgingdianneauthor@gmail.com. I look forward to hearing from you.

Namaste

The light in me honors the light in you.

May this book help your light shine brighter.

References

Janesksela, J. (2018, January 3). Why you should make visualization a daily practice. *Success.*

Niles, F. (2011, August 17). How to use visualization to achieve your goals. *Huff Post.* https://www.huffpost.com/entry/visualization-goals_b_878424

Appendix 1: List of Suggested Intentions

Typically, I prefer to let participants choose their own intention for their practice because I feel it's something very personal. Sometimes, I offer suggestions, but ultimately, I leave it up to each individual, referring to it as "your intention" throughout the practice. The following is a list of possible intentions for each chapter. Most overlap into more than one category.

	Focus & Engagement	Self Confidence & Acceptance	Gratitude	Letting Go & Trust	Relaxation
Abundance			X		
Acceptance		X		X	
Appreciation		X	X		X
Awareness	X	X			X
Balance	X			X	
Be kind to yourself		X			
Believe				X	
Braveness		X		X	
Breath	X	X	X	X	X
Calmness				X	X
Caring		X		X	
Clarity	X			X	

Connection		X			X
Courage		X		X	
Delight	X	X	X		
Empathy		X		X	
Endurance	X				
Essential	X				
Exploration		X		X	
Faith		X		X	X
Flexibility				X	
Forgiveness		X		X	
Freedom	X	X	X	X	X
Give			X		
Give & Take		X	X	X	
Grace				X	X
Gratitude	X	X	X	X	X
Growth	X	X	X	X	
Harmony		X		X	X
Healing	X	X		X	X
Honesty	X	X			
I am worthy	X	X	X		
Important	X	X	X	X	
Integrity		X	X		

Joy	X	X	X	X	X
Keep it Simple	X			X	X
Kindness	X	X	X		
Letting Go				X	X
Lightness	X	X	X	X	X
Live in the moment	X		X	X	X
Now	X		X	X	X
Patience	X	X			X
Peace		X	X	X	X
Persistence	X	X			
Productivity	X	X			
Receive		X	X	X	X
Resilience	X	X		X	
Restoring	X	X		X	X
Self-Care	X	X		X	X
Serenity			X	X	X
Tranquility				X	X
Trust				X	X
Value	X	X	X	X	X
Wisdom	X	X			
Wonder	X	X	X		

Acknowledgments

I would like to acknowledge my phenomenal yoga teacher and friend, Pamela Harrington, who continues to support me in both my yoga and personal journeys, and to Cheryl, who holds me accountable during each step of my journey.

I would also like to acknowledge Self-Publishing School, and those specifically who guided my journey; I would like to list them all, but I am afraid I would miss someone. All of the personnel I encountered went out of their way to be helpful and supportive, both at professional and personal levels. I could not have done it without their encouragement and expertise.

Thank you to all the wonderful teachers I work with on a daily basis, whose laughter and support inspire and motivate me. Thank you to our principal, who never fails to back us and to encourage us to take to risks and live dangerously. My gratitude extends to the other instructional coaches in our district, who feed my "professional soul" and inspire me be intentional about which "hills to die on".

I dedicated this book to my supporting family, but would be remiss not to acknowledge them again. You are my reason for being, and I am blessed to have each of you in my life. An extra shout out to my husband, who never failed to believe I could make this happen, and supported me through all of my doubts and frustrations along the way. Thank you.

Finally, thank you to all my friends, who each play a valuable part in my journey. I cannot mention you all, but know how important you have been in my journey. You are the best parts of me.

I am truly blessed.

Namaste

NOW IT'S YOUR TURN

Discover the EXACT 3-step blueprint you need to become a bestselling author in as little as 3 months.

Self-Publishing School helped me, and now I want them to help you with this FREE resource to begin outlining your book!

Even if you're busy, bad at writing, or don't know where to start, you CAN write a bestseller and build your best life.

With tools and experience across a variety of niches and professions, Self-Publishing School is the only resource you need to take your book to the finish line!

DON'T WAIT

Say "YES" to becoming a bestseller:

https://self-publishingschool.com/friend/

Follow the steps on the page to get a FREE resource to get started on your book and unlock a discount to get started with Self-Publishing School.

ABOUT THE AUTHOR

Dianne Willging has worked in the field of education for over thirty years in a variety of capacities. She began her journey in yoga as a result of managing back pain, and found it added so much more to her physical and mental health.

Some of these benefits include strength, flexibility, focus, stress relief, and reflection. Dianne is a certified yoga teacher, who strives to balance the physical asanas, or poses, with the other limbs of yoga. The use of visualization within her yoga practice has greatly enhanced her life, and she seeks to share this tool with other people on their journey to a more focused, peaceful state of being. This is her first book.

Can You Help?

Thank You for Reading My Book!

I really appreciate all of your feedback, and I love hearing what you have to say.

I need your input to make the next version of this book and my future books better.

Please leave me an honest review on Amazon letting me know what you thought of the book.

Thanks so much!

Namaste

–Dianne Willging